THE BAKER STREET IRREGULARS

THE ADVENTURE OF THE

MISSING DETECTIVE

TONY LEE and DAN BOULTWOOD

EDGE
FRANKLIN
WATTS

LONDON·SYDNEY

First published in 2011 by
Franklin Watts
338 Euston Road
London NW1 3BH

Franklin Watts Australia
Level 17/207 Kent Street
Sydney, NSW 2000

Text © Tony Lee 2011
Illustrations © Dan Boultwood 2011
Cover design by Jonathan Hair
"The Baker Street Irregulars" logo
designed by Patrick Insole

Special thanks to Leslie S. Klinger for his invaluable contribution to this series

"Baker Street Irregulars" and the original characters
"Dr Watson", "Inspector Lestrade", "Irene Adler",
"Wiggins", "Moriarty" and "Sherlock Holmes"
the creation of Sir Arthur Conan Doyle.

A CIP catalogue record for this book
is available from the British Library

ISBN: 978 1 4451 0342 6

3 5 7 9 10 8 6 4

Printed in China

Franklin Watts is a division of Hachette Children's Books,
an Hachette UK company
www.hachette.co.uk

THE ADVENTURE OF THE
MISSING DETECTIVE

The story so far...

Sherlock Holmes is *missing*, assumed *dead*. He is believed to have fallen to his death over the *Reichenbach Falls* while fighting his arch enemy, *Professor Moriarty*. Without Holmes, London is in danger of becoming a *lawless* city - despite the efforts of the famous *Inspector Lestrade*.

But there are others ready to step *into* the shoes of the great detective - *Wiggins*, Holmes's teenage protégé and his companions *The Baker Street Irregulars* still solve the crimes that Holmes once examined, hoping that the great detective *isn't* dead - but it's a hope that fades with every passing day...

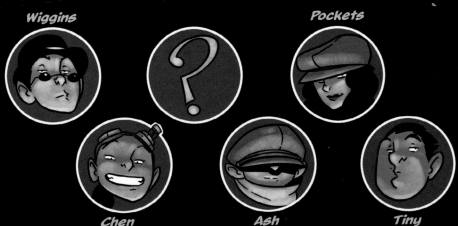

Wiggins

Pockets

Chen

Ash

Tiny

Later.

Thank you for your words, Lestrade. They were, well, *short and to the point.*

Not at all, Doctor Watson. I felt that I owed it to --

Doctor Watson! Inspector Lestrade! Wait! Please!

Aha - you remember young *Wiggins*, don't you Inspector? You first met during the *Stangerson** murder?

*From A Study in Scarlet, the first *Sherlock Holmes* adventure.

I do - but that was *ten years ago!* This boy must have been no more than *six years old* back then!

I was, sir - but six years old and living on the *streets of London* – you grow up fast!

Sherlock Holmes took me under his wing, trained me up to be a *detective* - and that's why we're here!

We don't think that Mister Holmes is *dead* - and we want to *reopen the case!*

You *do,* do you? You and who else?

The Baker Street Irregulars.

Pockets, the fastest lockpicker in London.

Chen, one of the greatest inventors in the city.

Tiny, a big artist with an even bigger heart –

- and his little brother *Ash,* a chimney sweep apprentice who can slip down a rabbit hole!

So. A *pickpocket*, the nephew of a *Tong gang leader* - yes, I know who you are, *Chen Sin-Hau* -

- as well as a *bruiser* and a *burglar*. And then there's *you*, Wiggins.

You're not exactly squeaky clean yourself, are you? Son of notorious criminal *Morris Wiggins* --

I'm not my *father*, Inspector. And he's been in prison for the last *six years*.

Now - are you going to *help* us find Sherlock Holmes - or simply *state our faults* again?

There's nothing to find, lad - he's *gone*.

Inspector, sir - *message* for you.

Wiggins - I know that Holmes was like a *father figure* to all of you - but there are points where you must simply accept the --

Where's *Mycroft Holmes* today? Where's the *brother* of Sherlock Holmes? Not here!

He didn't come - because he knows that *Sherlock Holmes isn't dead!*

I'm sorry, Doctor Watson - I'll have to take my final look at *221b Baker Street* some other time.

We've received information that the *daughter* of the *Lord Mayor of London* has just been *kidnapped*.

6

My name's *Eliza Mayhew* - my grandfather is *Richard Mayhew,* the detective. You were rivals on a case, I believe?

Yes, the *Rathbone* mystery. It was only briefly. I can't see what that has to do with --

I'm very worried - my grandfather is *missing*, Doctor Watson.

He was agitated about something when I last saw him three days ago, but he wouldn't say what it was -

- and then two days ago witnesses saw him being bundled by two men *into the back of a carriage!*

My parents died when I was *two* - my grandfather is all I have in the world!

I have to find him! I know Sherlock Holmes is gone, but you *assisted* him - surely you can --

My dear girl! I'm no detective! I'm a simple doctor.

All I ever did was record Holmes's career! I'm sorry, but there's nothing we can do --

I'll take your case, Miss Eliza.

What?

13

Chen, Tiny - you come with me.

Ash, Eliza - you return to *Baker Street* and tell Wiggins what we've found out.

But my grandfather might be *in* there! I'm coming in with you!

He taught me *everything* - I'm just as good a detective as *you* are!

That you might be - but you're also the *client* - and we're about to break into a house.

So *be* a client and go with Ash. We'll let you know as soon as we find anything.

That was a little *harsh*, Pockets! Why couldn't she come in here to find her grandfather?

Because we don't know if he *is* in here, Tiny - and worse than that --

-- we don't know what *state* he's in. What if he's *dead*?

We can't let her see *that* now, can we?

Right then. Let's find this *missing detective* - and then get out fast.

The *last* thing we want is a *Lestrade* visit.

14

FLUFFY!

WHAM!

GRRRRR

Come on! It's a *monster!* We gotta get out of here!

Good boy! How did you get free?

Looks like somebody *cut your rope!* Who did this?

One of the bullies dropped this as he fell - it might be a *clue!*

Come on, boy - let's get back to Baker Street!

Good dog.

'M' for *Moriarty*, I reckon. Someone's keeping his name alive.

But if it *is* him, then I'll wager he's also involved with the *kidnapping* too.

But I thought Moriarty supposedly *died* with *Sherlock Holmes?*

The two men Peabody describes sound just like the two thugs who *attacked* me —

— but neither of them had a weapon like *that.*

It wasn't just two men — witnesses saw a *third* leave the building.

A *tall, thin* man — wore a *top hat*, held a *cane* —

— and had a *scarf* that covered the *bottom half* of his face.

Now, if you don't mind — the body has been *identified*, and now the *real police* can do some work.

Come on, *out* with you.

Before you go — I have something for young Miss Eliza, if you would pass it to her?

Her grandfather wrote it for her *last night* — just before his death.

25

Baker Street.

So what does it say?

I don't know... Hold on --

My dearest **Eliza**, if you read this, it means I have **died** before I could speak to you -

- before I could tell you the **terrible truth** about your identity.

"... Many years ago, I was a **bad** man. One of the worst out there - and with my two friends, **Lucas** and **Arthur** --"

"-- we ran the greatest **kidnapping scheme** in the north of England."

"The children of the rich were our **targets** - easy money to make. But we had foolishly chosen not to wear masks --"

"-- and we were easily **recognised**."

"It was when we kidnapped you that the **problems** started. Yes, Eliza, you were the daughter of a **rich businessman,** not my grandaughter."

"Lucas was recognised in York, and he wanted to finish up and leave immediately - but before doing so, he would kill our **latest witness** - "

"you."

"I couldn't let them do that - and I knew that if I took you home, Lucas would **find** you. And so I **ran**, taking you with me."

"I called the police and left an **anonymous tip** - Lucas and Arthur were **arrested** and sentenced to **ten years** each."

"I brought you here to **London** where, changing my **name** --"

"-- I reinvented myself as an **amateur detective**."

"All these years I have wanted to **tell** you this - but I have been **ashamed**, and scared of **losing you**. You have been like a daughter to me."

"I have never **regretted** saving you, even though it meant causing your family pain."

"But now my past has caught up with me. Lucas and Arthur have **found** me, and I fear for **your** life more than mine."

I couldn't tell you my plans, in case it led them to **you** - so instead I arranged for my own abduction.

I am **so sorry** for all that I have done in my life - **you** are the one shining point in it.

After all these years I have forgotten your **true** parents' name - and even the surname '**Mayhew**' is a lie, one that I picked on a train --

-- but you will **always** be **my Eliza Mayhew**.

You're wrong, Eliza - by blood or not, he *was* your grandfather, and he protected you to the end.

He wasn't my grandfather! Somewhere out there I have a *family!*

So now we *honour* him by finding his *killers.*

All we have to *do* is work out this *code.*

Are they cab numbers? Like on the back of a *hansom cab?*

I wanna see! Is very *important* that I see! I may know!

Ash! You've got *soot* on it now!

No! Look --

Aww, it's *boring.*

-- Ash's smudge turned it into a *time!* And those numbers beside it are a date! *Today's* date!

12 34

Where's the **Bradshaw** book? That has all the train timetables in it! I've seen Mister Holmes use it!

It could also be a timetable for a **boat** or **coach?**

True, but these two **came** from up North, and I believe they're going **back!**

They have the **Lord Mayor's daughter,** and they're taking her to York - where they hid their kidnap victims **over ten years ago!**

There! A train to **York** from **King's Cross** at that exact time! They're on that train, I know it - and I reckon they're back to their old games!

Ash - take Fluffy and go to **Lestrade.** Tell him what we've discovered!

Chen - get your bag of **tricks!** We may need some of them!

We need to get on that **train!** Pockets, you've seen their faces - you can lead us!

What about this **masked man** that Lestrade mentioned? If he **is** the man who left the card that said **'M',** what if **he's** on the train?

If this mysterious 'M' **is** there - then **he'll pay** for Richard Mayhew's death.

And if he really is **Moriarty** - then he'll answer to **Sherlock Holmes's** friends.

What are you *holding*, Chen?

Hurry — the train's about to leave!

A rocket! I built this so that when we capture the criminals, we can fire it into the sky so that *Inspector Lestrade* knows!

If he even bothers to *come,* that is! He hasn't believed us before!

I also sent a message with Mrs Hudson — *Doctor Watson* is on his way to Lestrade as well!

Right ho, then — let's find the *kidnappers!*

30

The 12.34 train to York.

That was *too close!* Now, where was I --

I don't want to have to *fight* you --

You! Stay where you are!

You may not, boy --

-- but I do.

KRACK!

⸗ Hnf ⸗

Look, Daddy! It's a *flying boy!*

Yes, dear - of *course* it is.

35

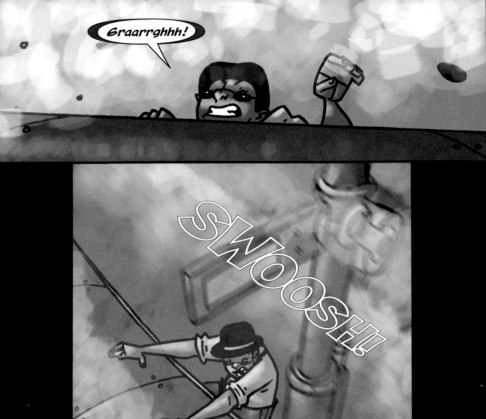

Of *course* I am grateful for your *minor* assistance in this case, and I will be sure to pass on your names to the Lord Mayor.

Holmes heard similar from him *all the time.*

That's Lestrade's way of saying, 'Thank you for *solving* this case.'

We should get back to London - the Mayor will want his child back as quickly as possible.

What about 'M'? We need to find his *body* - see if he *was* Moriarty!

However, there were signs of someone *leaving* the water. I believe that this 'M' is still *alive.*

We sent some men to the lake - but there was *no sign* of a body.

He *survived?* How can that be!

If it *was* Moriarty, that's *two* watery deaths that he's escaped! The man must be *half fish!*

Come on, let's get out of here before the guard realises that *we never had tickets!*

The Diogenes Club.

Very nice piece on you in *The Times of London.* That should bring in some clients.

And a *new hat,* I see.

Yes, Doctor Watson bought it for me.

I briefly considered a *deerstalker* hat like Holmes wore -

- but I look *silly* in those.

We made a *deal.* You promised to tell me the truth.

I did - and you kept your end of the deal.

But these words are for you, and *you* alone.

Sherlock Holmes *isn't* dead - he's currently travelling across the globe. Moriarty's men saw him *survive* - and now he is *hiding,* in case they take revenge on *Doctor Watson.*

He intends to spend the next few years quietly taking each member of Moriarty's gang *down* - until the day he can return.

Of course! And that's why 'M' is in London - if it *is* Moriarty, then --

There's no proof that it *is,* Wiggins. Moriarty is *still* most likely *dead.*

Be wary of *assuming* things. Stick to *facts.* We can't have a detective in Baker Street who simply *guesses!*

I might as well move *Lestrade* in, if that was the case!

You mean that we can *stay there?* Thank you!

You're a worthy *stand in* until my brother returns. And it'll give us a chance to watch over *Watson* and his family.

Mrs Hudson has already been made aware of the changes. Go now and *detect*, my dear boy.

Thank you! Thank you! *You won't regret this!*

You *might* regret that decision, you know.

I'm just helping the boy to stand on his own two feet.

My brother made the *right choice* when he took young Wiggins into his care.

Helping solve *crimes* - annoying Doctor Watson -

- I might have some *fun* after all.

You might need to spend a little *longer* watching over this flock, Irene. Is that *agreeable* with you?

Well, I didn't have anything *else* to do for a while, so I'm sure that I can spend some time in London.

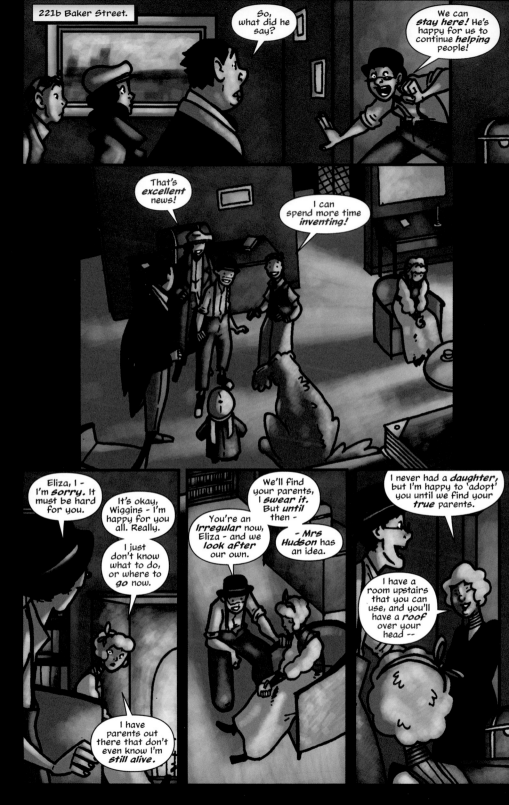

221b Baker Street.

So, what did he say?

We can **stay here!** He's happy for us to continue **helping** people!

That's **excellent** news!

I can spend more time **inventing!**

Eliza, I - I'm **sorry.** It must be hard for you.

It's okay, Wiggins - I'm happy for you all. Really.

I just don't know what to do, or where to **go** now.

I have parents out there that don't even know I'm **still alive.**

We'll find your parents, I **swear it.** But **until** then -

You're an **Irregular** now, Eliza - and we **look after** our own.

- Mrs **Hudson** has an idea.

I never had a **daughter,** but I'm happy to 'adopt' you until we find your **true** parents.

I have a room upstairs that you can use, and you'll have a **roof** over your head --

"I hope that the *next* one is as *interesting* as this one was!"

Blimey, I don't half *hate this place* at night!

Drury Lane Theatre, London.

It right gives me the *creeps*, it does! All those *ghosts* and stories --

Exactly! *Stories!* Don't get turned around and all inside out because of *ghost tales!*

There ain't no *ghost* of Drury Lane --

-- there never *has been*, and there never *will be!*

NEXT: DON'T MISS BOOK TWO - *THE ADVENTURE OF THE PHANTOM OF DRURY LANE!*

THE BAKER STREET
IRREGULARS

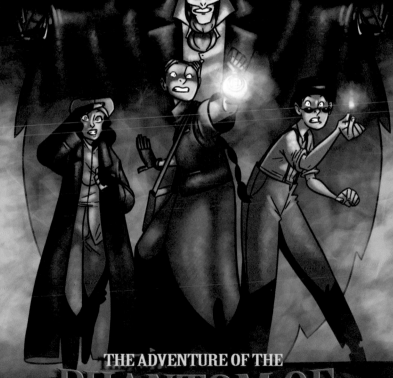

THE ADVENTURE OF THE
PHANTOM OF
DRURY LANE

TONY LEE and DAN BOULTWOOD

978 1 4451 0343 3 pb   978 1 4451 1423 1 eBook